Maths Puzzles

My name is ....

....

I am .... years old.

I go to .... school.

I am .... at Maths!

Juliet and Charles Snape

Collins

Alien Pal

Can you help me find my pal Roger?

Roger is floating somewhere in the Alien Parade. On his left and right sides are one-eyed aliens, above him floats a four-eyed alien and a two-eyed alien is below. *Which one is Roger?*

Which of these facts about the Alien Parade is false?

1. The three-eyed green aliens have 42 eyes altogether.
2. Altogether, there are more blue fingers than pink fingers.
3. There are 120 yellow arms.

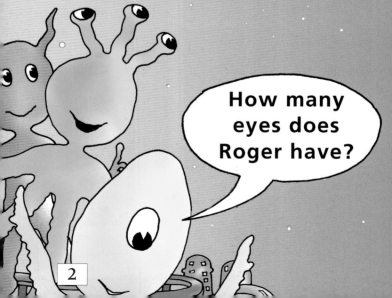

How many eyes does Roger have?

TIMES FOR THE TABLE...

At Greater Snoring's Village Fair, all the prizes at the tombola table are numbered with multiples of 7...

GREATER SNORING THE TOMBOLA

TAKE 7 AND DOUBLE IT

7 TIMES 3

DOUBLE 7, AND DOUBLE AGAIN

BUNNY'S LUNCH

SID'S CHEESY SOCKS

PURE FRESH AIR

GREATER SNORING FRESH AIR

3 TIMES 7 AND DOUBLE IT

MYSTERY BOX

10 TIMES 7 AND HALVE IT

Appletree FARM

BEAUTY MUD PACK

THE 7 MOVES INTO THE 10's POSITION

WASH UP LIQU

I got 7 × 7

BUBBLE BATH

10 TIMES 7, THEN TAKE AWAY 7

ETHEL'S WINTER HAT (+MOTH)

2 TIMES 7, DOUBLE AND DOUBLE AGAIN

TOOTH BRUSH OF NELLY (THE HORSE)

7 SQUARED

FRED'S SANDWICH

ALL PRIZES KINDLY DONATED

?

49

Match the winning tickets to the prizes.

☐ Greater Snoring fresh air	☐ Bubble bath	☐ Fred's sandwich
☐ Sid's cheesy socks	☐ Beauty mud pack	☐ Toothbrush of Nelly
☐ Bunny's lunch	☐ Mystery box	☐ Ethel's winter hat

MULTIPLICATION MADE EASY

✴ If you know one fact, you know another:
e.g. 3 × 7 is the same as 7 × 3

✴ DOUBLING
Doubling makes the 4 and 8 times tables as easy as the 2 times table:
e.g. 2 × 7 = 14
doubling 14 gives you
4 × 7 = 28
double again, you get
8 × 7 = 56

✴ HALVING
If you can multiply by 10, then you can multiply by 5:
e.g. 7 × 10 = 70
halve 70... that's 35
so 7 × 5 = 35

✴ If you know 9 is one less than 10, then you can multiply by 9:
e.g. 7 × 10 = 70
take one 7 away from 70 and you get 7 × 9 = 63

Pirate Positions

The four main points on the compass are N, S, E, W (north, south, east and west).

Wherever you are in the world, the arrow of a magnetic compass points towards the North Pole. When you are facing north, east is the direction to your right. When you are facing south, the direction on your right is west.

Halfway between each of the main compass points are the directions NE (north-east), SE (south-east), SW (south-west) and NW (north-west).

At Port Plunder, pirates gather to dispose of their booty. The port is full of puzzles. To solve them you will need logic and compass directions.

Each puzzle contains all the clues you need to solve it. Look for the compass to find where north is.

It will help to get some small pieces of paper and write the names on them. Move them around until you think you have the answer, then check if all the clues still fit.

1

Which is Polly Parrot?

☠ Pesky Parrot is east of Pretty Parrot.

☠ Polly Parrot is west of Pretty Parrot.

Find Red Rob!

☠ Dirty Derek is north-west of Sleepy Sam.

☠ Mad Pete is east of Dirty Derek.

2

3

Find the sherry

- ☠ The rum is between the sherry and the beer.
- ☠ The beer is west of the rum.
- ☠ The brandy is east of the sherry.

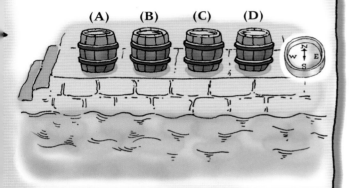

(A) (B) (C) (D)

Where are the rubies?

- ☠ The chest of gold is north of the silver.
- ☠ The silver is west of the diamonds.
- ☠ The pearls are south-west of the gold.

5

4

Where's the treasure?

- ☠ The treasure isn't buried east of the trees.
- ☠ It isn't buried west of the boat.
- ☠ It is not south-east of the hut.

Which is the Black Dog?

- ☠ The pirates' ship, the Black Dog, is east of the Gritty Shark, and alongside it.
- ☠ The Dodgy Dolphin is west of the Black Dog and south of the Slinky Sole.
- ☠ The Fighting Fish is east of the rest.

6

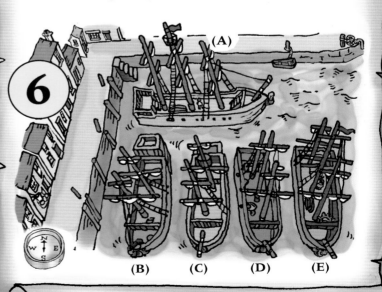

Detective De Duction

The detective has some logic and number puzzles to solve... can you help

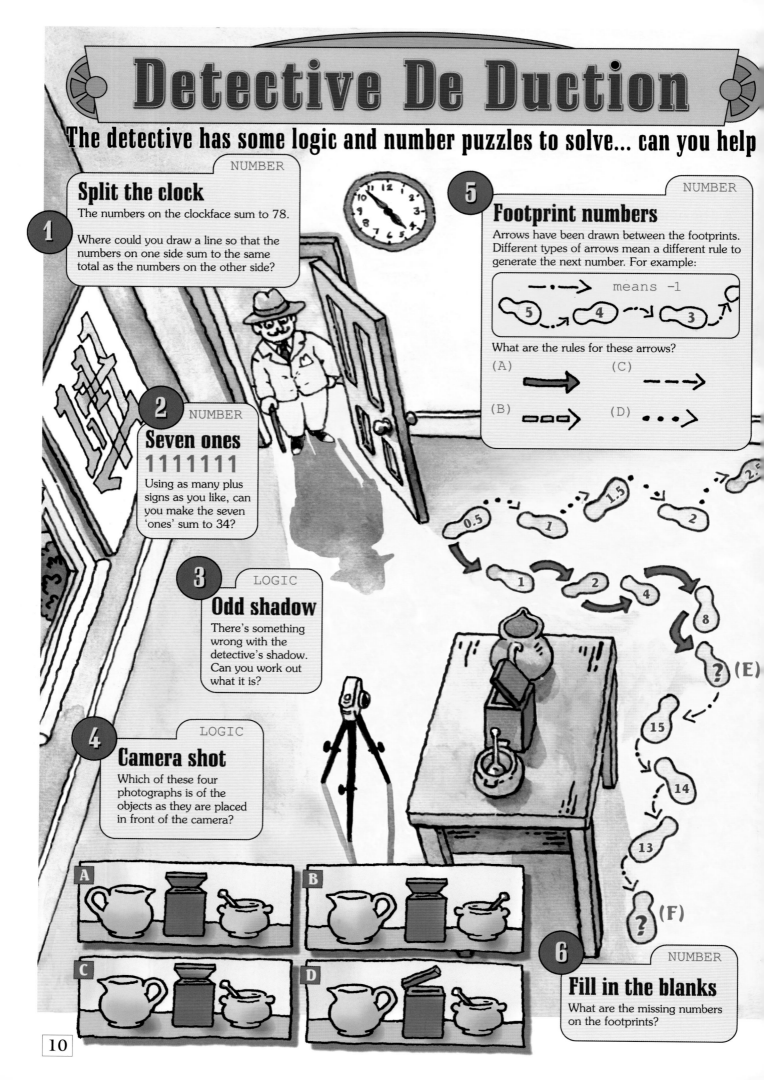

1

NUMBER

Split the clock

The numbers on the clockface sum to 78.

Where could you draw a line so that the numbers on one side sum to the same total as the numbers on the other side?

2

NUMBER

Seven ones
1111111

Using as many plus signs as you like, can you make the seven 'ones' sum to 34?

3

LOGIC

Odd shadow

There's something wrong with the detective's shadow. Can you work out what it is?

4

LOGIC

Camera shot

Which of these four photographs is of the objects as they are placed in front of the camera?

5

NUMBER

Footprint numbers

Arrows have been drawn between the footprints. Different types of arrows mean a different rule to generate the next number. For example:

```
--·--->   means -1
```
5 → 4 → 3

What are the rules for these arrows?

(A) ⟶

(B) ▭▭▭⟩

(C) - - - ⟶

(D) • • • ⟩

6

NUMBER

Fill in the blanks

What are the missing numbers on the footprints?

(1)

(2)

(3)

(4)

7 Picture shapes

Pick the shape from the ones below that best fits in the bottom right-hand corner of each picture.

(A)   (B)   (C)   (D)   (E)   (F)

8 Missing jewel

From these three jewels…

(A)   (B)   (C)

… which one belongs to the necklace in the chest?

9 Which key?

The correct key to the padlock is not one of a pair. Which key is it?

(A)
(B)
(C)
(D)
(E)
(F)
(G)
(H)
(I)

10 Name the set

Which of these labels best describes the set of shapes on the rug below?

- circles
- all red
- triangles
- not squares

3.5
3
(G) ?
2
1
0.5
(H) ?
1.25
2.25
(I) ?
6.5
13
(J) ?

11 Squares within squares

How many squares can you find here?

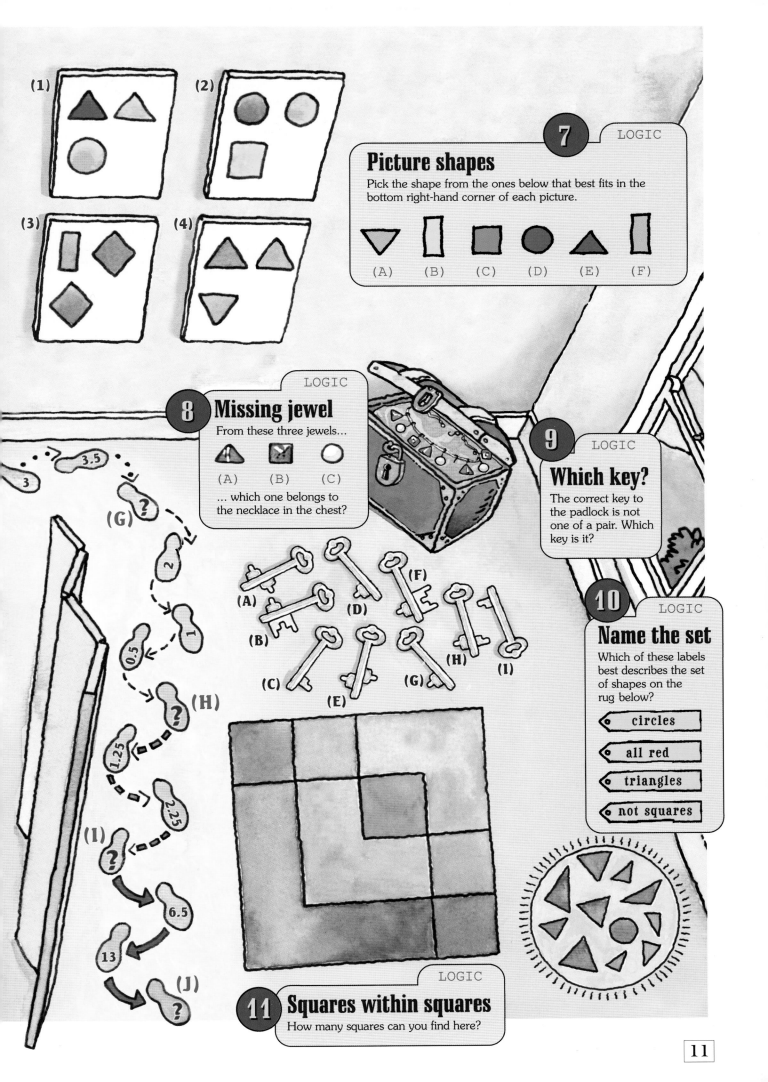

11

Highway Robbery?

Bad Bob is a highway man. His old horse 'Potbelly' doesn't like to go very far, so Bad Bob only robs coaches that travel the road between Castle Town and Marsh Point.

The mail coach takes three different routes each week. It always leaves and returns to the Swan Inn. It must go through Castle Town and Ports Town but the coach never goes through the same place twice on a journey. The coach travels at 10 km per hour.

Swan Inn

Look at the coach route details below (Routes 1, 2 and 3).

(A) Can you find the three routes from the information given?
REMEMBER: Each route must go through both Castle Town and Ports Town.

(B) Does Bad Bob ever get to rob the mail coach?

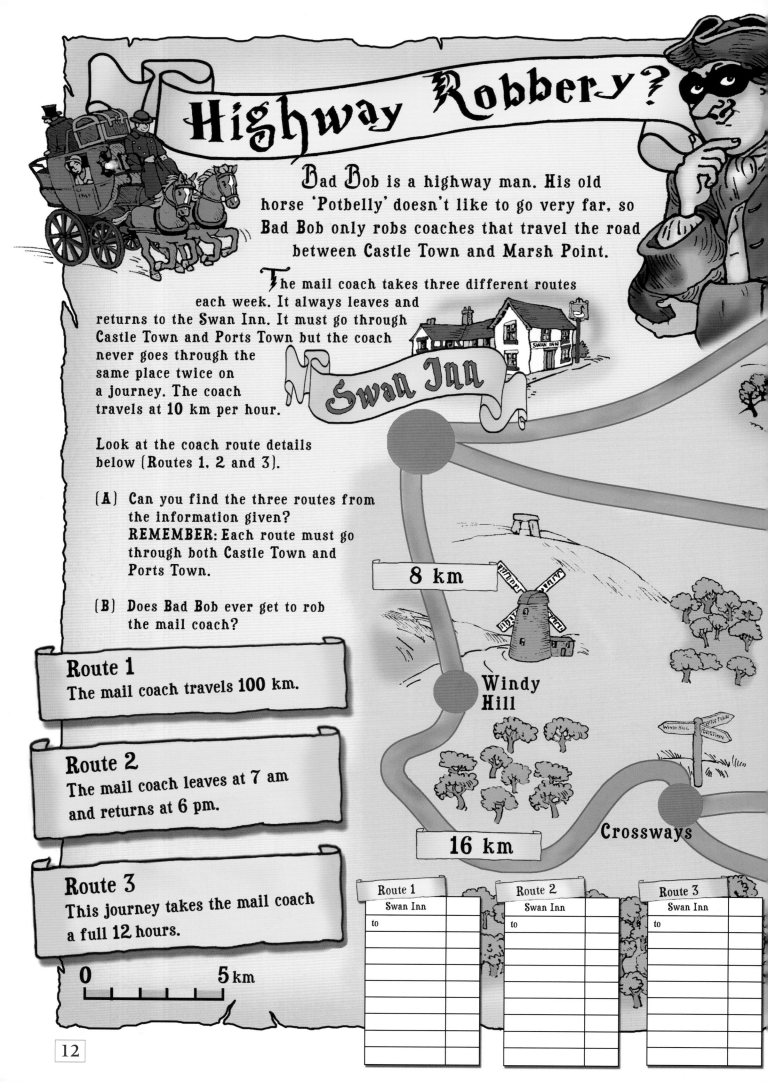

8 km

Windy Hill

16 km

Crossways

Route 1
The mail coach travels **100 km.**

Route 2
The mail coach leaves at **7 am** and returns at **6 pm.**

Route 3
This journey takes the mail coach a full **12 hours.**

0   5 km

Route 1	
Swan Inn	
to	

Route 2	
Swan Inn	
to	

Route 3	
Swan Inn	
to	

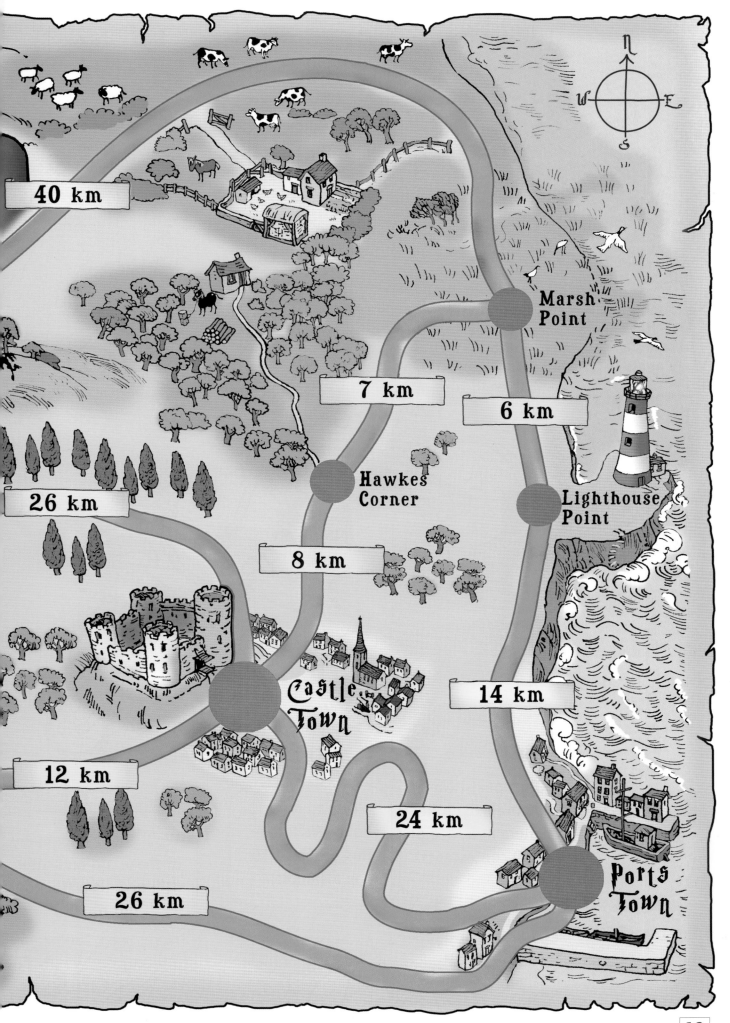

40 km

Marsh
Point

7 km

6 km

26 km

Hawkes
Corner

Lighthouse
Point

8 km

Castle
Town

12 km

14 km

24 km

26 km

Ports
Town

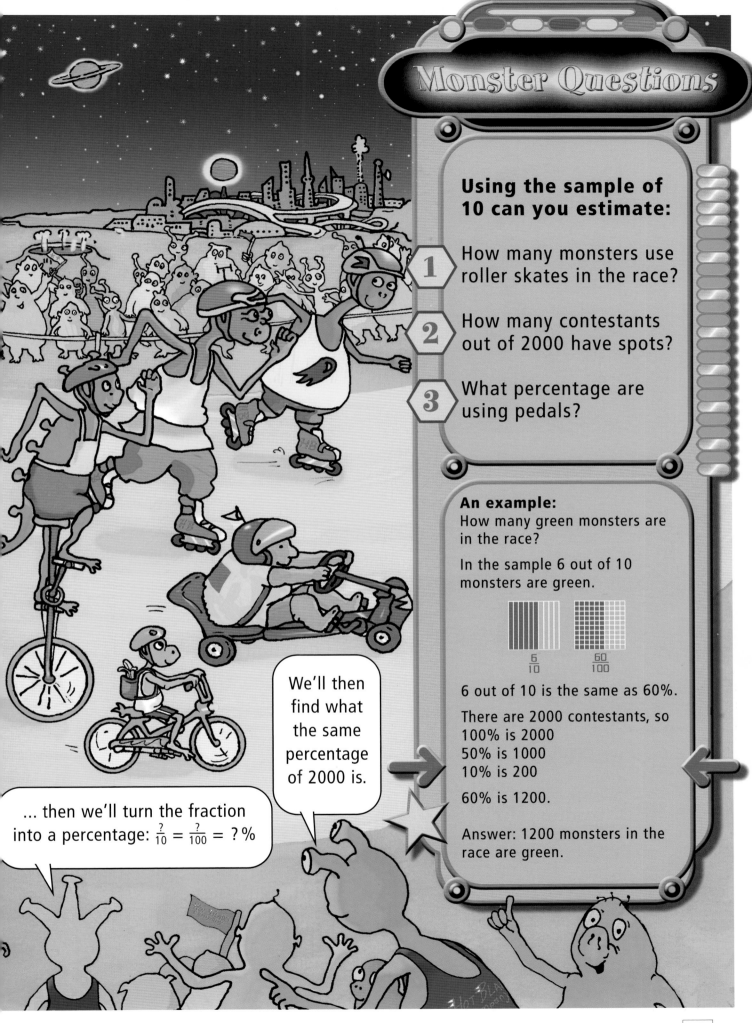

Monster Questions

Using the sample of 10 can you estimate:

1 How many monsters use roller skates in the race?

2 How many contestants out of 2000 have spots?

3 What percentage are using pedals?

An example:
How many green monsters are in the race?

In the sample 6 out of 10 monsters are green.

$$\frac{6}{10} \qquad \frac{60}{100}$$

6 out of 10 is the same as 60%.

There are 2000 contestants, so
100% is 2000
50% is 1000
10% is 200

60% is 1200.

Answer: 1200 monsters in the race are green.

We'll then find what the same percentage of 2000 is.

... then we'll turn the fraction into a percentage: $\frac{?}{10} = \frac{?}{100} = ?\%$

WHAT'S THE DISTANCE?

Send for help... QUICK!

Loonius, the Pro-consul of the long forgotten province of Pomposium, lives in Circadium. Find it in the picture below.

Loonius is having trouble. There are three people who can help: Molia of Aquarium, Decayius of Odearium and Cavitus of Eggium.

(1) Who is nearest?
   To work it out look at the distance table.

(2) Can you work out which of the three towns i
   which in the picture? Hints: Which town is
   nearest to Tiptopium (by road)? Which town
   is nearest to Ohmyium?
   Use the distance table.

(3) Answer the questions on the milestone and
   discover why Loonius needs help.

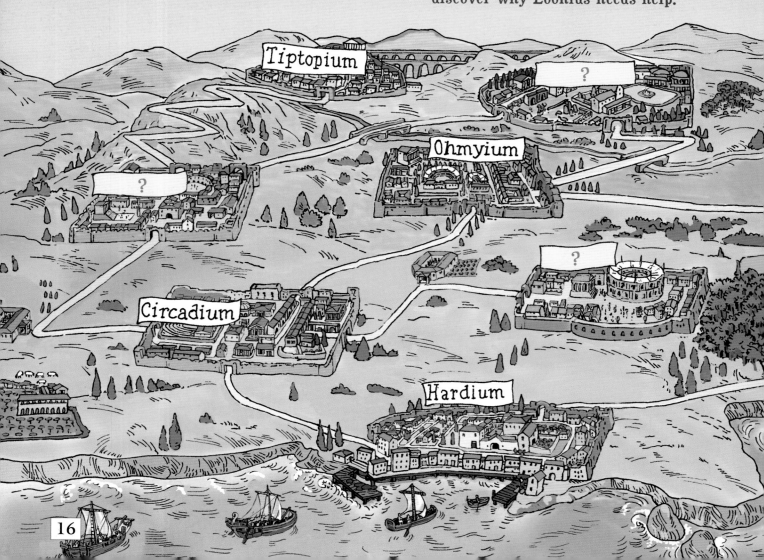

Distance by road between towns (milia passuum*)

Aquarium							
37	Caromello						
30	33	Circadium					
47	50	17	Eggium				
40	30	10	27	Hardium			
23	53	20	37	30	Odearium		
17	20	13	30	23	33	Ohmyium	
46	76	43	60	53	23	56	Tiptopium

* milia passuum (Latin for **1000** paces) are Roman miles

This table gives distances along the roads and **NOT** as the crow flies.

This is a distance table. You can use it to find the distances along the roads between all the different towns. Follow down the column of one town and along the row of another: the rectangle where they meet gives the number of milia passuum.

Aquarium			
37	Caromello		
30	33	Circadium	
	50	17	Eggium
40			27	Hardium
23	33	20	30

Example: Aquarium to Hardium is 40 milia passuum.

Use data from the distance table to answer these questions. Put the first letter of the town in each box to reveal the problem that Loonius has.

Town letter

1. Which town is furthest from Circadium?

2. Which town is nearest to Tiptopium?

3. Which town is 17 milia passuum from Aquarium?

4. Which town is furthest from Hardium?

5. Which town is nearest to Circadium?

6. Which town is 30 milia passuum from Circadium?

7. Which town is 20 milia passuum from Ohmyium?

8. Which town is 30 milia passuum from Caromello?

9. Which town is 37 milia passuum from Odearium?

17

Coordinates in the Castle

The people in the castle are all taking mathematical walks in the courtyard. Their paths will each make the shape of a different type of quadrilateral. Each path can be plotted with coordinates using the grid.

Coordinates give the point where two lines meet. For example, the basket of cabbages is at (15, 7). To find a point using pairs of coordinates, find the first number (15, 7) across the horizontal axis at

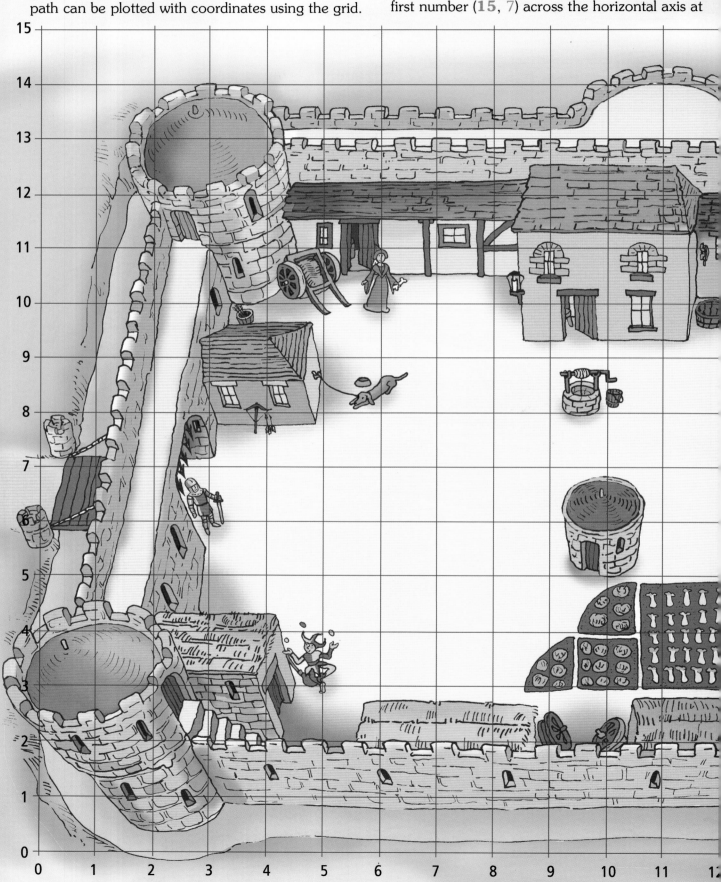

the bottom of the grid. Then find the second number (15, **7**) up the vertical axis at the side.

Use the 'Quadrilaterals File' to work out who is making which type of quadrilateral. *Which one is not made?*

Use tracing paper to plot each path on the coordinates grid.

Martha the maiden is going to give the dog a bone. She starts at (6, 10) then (8, 9) (6, 6) (5, 8) then back to (6, 10).

John the jester is practising his dance. His path is: (5, 3) (8, 3) (8, 6) (5, 6) then back to (5, 3).

Friar Doug is gardening. He goes from (14, 5) to (12, 5) (10, 8) (15, 8) then back to (14, 5).

Graham the guard needs to stretch his legs. He marches from (3, 6) to (9, 6) (9, 7) (3, 7) then back to (3, 6).

Sarah the cook is carrying a tub. She goes from (15, 9) to (9, 9) (7, 7) (13, 7) then back to (15, 9).

If the guard pauses at (8, 7) who will he meet?

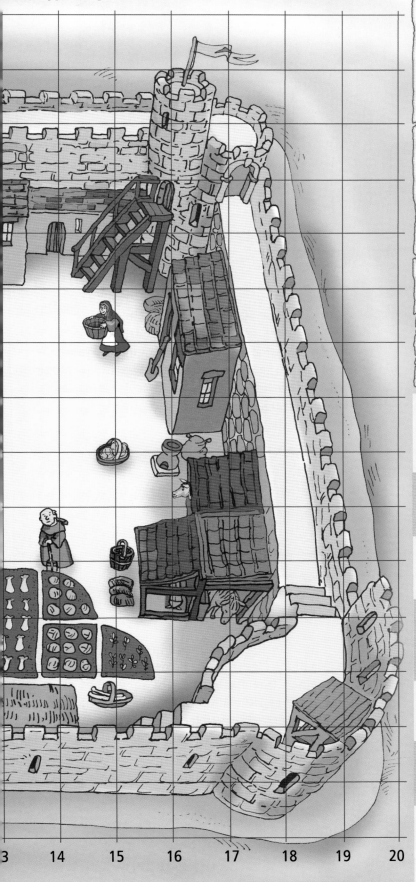

3   14   15   16   17   18   19   20

Quadrilaterals File

A quadrilateral is any shape with 4 straight lines.

Irregular quadrilateral — A shape with 4 straight sides.

Trapezium — A trapezium has one pair of parallel lines (shown by arrowheads).

Parallelogram — A parallelogram has two pairs of parallel lines (the second pair is shown by double arrowheads). Pairs of sides of equal length are shown with short lines (two short lines are used for a second pair).

Rhombus — A rhombus is a parallelogram with all sides equal in length.

Square — A square is a rhombus with four right angles (shown by a small square in each corner).

Rectangle — A rectangle has opposite sides equal and each angle is a right angle.

19

I didn't mean that kind of axes!

The Romans' idea of a good day out produces some...

GRUESOME GRAPHS

Graphs and diagrams can show data in a visual way. They make the information easier to understand.

Here are some types you might see.

Line Graphs and Bar Graphs need:
- axes at right angles
- labels to say what each axis shows
- a title.

1. Line Graph

Varying speed of a chariot in a race

speed of the chariot km/h

50
40
30
20
10
0

1 2 3 4 5 6 7
laps in the race

Line graphs show changes over a continuous period of time. They are useful for recording many things, from temperature changes to sales figures.

White knuckle-ride

At the Circus Maximus, chariots raced at breakneck speed seven times around a track almost 2 km long. The young charioteers had the reins tied around their waists and if the chariot overturned they would be dragged along the racetrack. There were few rules and many collisions!

2. Pictograph

The emperor's decisions at the Games

| Not killed | 👍 👍 👍 👍 |
| killed | 👎 |

KEY: 👍 (up or down) represents 10 defeated gladiators

Each symbol in a pictograph (sometimes called a pictogram) can represent a specific number and is a very visual way to show statistical data.

Thumbs up or thumbs down

Gladiator fights at the Colosseum were very popular. One gladiator might be weighed down with armour and the other only have a net and a trident. If a gladiator surrendered, the crowd would shout "mitte!" (let him go) or "iugula!" (cut his throat). The emperor would signal the decision with a thumbs up or a thumbs down.

PHEW

3. Bar Graph

Unnatural deaths of emperors over **400** years

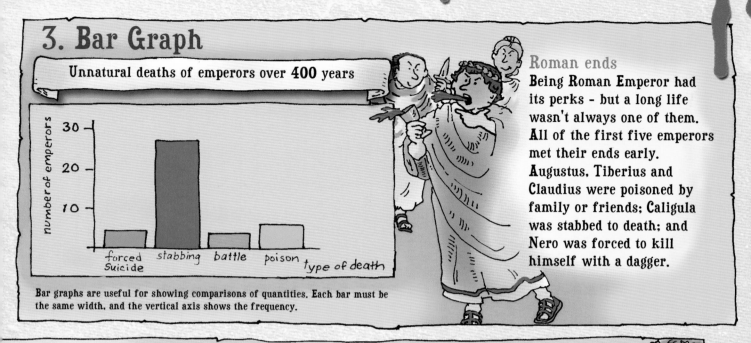

Bar graphs are useful for showing comparisons of quantities. Each bar must be the same width, and the vertical axis shows the frequency.

Roman ends

Being Roman Emperor had its perks - but a long life wasn't always one of them. All of the first five emperors met their ends early. Augustus, Tiberius and Claudius were poisoned by family or friends; Caligula was stabbed to death; and Nero was forced to kill himself with a dagger.

4. Pie Chart

How the money was spent at a day at the Games

A pie chart shows information by dividing up a circle into different 'slices'. It is very useful for showing how a 'whole' is made up.

Colossal costs

The building of the Colosseum in Rome took nine years and cost a fortune but the spending didn't stop there. The expense of a day at the Games was paid for by the patron (usually the emperor).
As well as gladiator combat, there were fights between prisoners and wild animals and hundreds of both were slaughtered. If a trained gladiator was killed, the patron had to compensate the gladiator school.
The public may have got in free but it usually cost an arm and a leg.

Can you answer these questions using the graphs?

1 In which lap did the chariot go the fastest?

2 How many of the 50 defeated gladiators got the thumbs up at the Games?

3 What was the most frequent cause of unnatural death of a Roman emperor in the first 400 years?

4 What was the least expense at the Games?

Add 'em up!

Tossing hoops, throwing darts and chucking balls into buckets adds up to all the fun of the fair!

SUM HOOPS

How to win: Throw three hoops and score 18. Can you find three ways to win?

Can you find 3 ways to make **20** exactly with three hoops?

8 6 2

SUM BUCKETS

How to win: Get four balls in the buckets and score exactly 600. Can you find three different ways to win?

Can you find 2 ways to make **450** exactly with four balls?

75 300 150

SUM DARTS

How to win: Use four darts and score **200** exactly.
Can you find three different ways to win?

Can you find 3 ways
to make **150** exactly
with four darts?

NOODLE NUTS

'Noodle Nuts' is a fast-food restaurant off Tokyo's main shopping street. It serves ramen (wheat noodles) which the Japanese just love to eat.

Find the answers to the problems of a typical working day at Noodle Nuts and discover, using the solutions panel opposite, what Hari said he liked best with his noodles.

NOODLE NUTS FACT

In Yokohama there is a museum, historical theme park and food mall entirely devoted to noodles.

Look, oodles of noodles!

04:30 Aiko goes to market for the fresh fish. Each bowl of prawn-noodles must have exactly 18 prawns. The tray contains 1500 prawns. If Aiko wants to make 100 bowls will one tray be enough?

Nice prawns! How many are here?

There are 1500 prawns in each tray.

NOODLE NUTS FACT

Eating out in Japan can be DEADLY! Over 20 people a year die from eating the wrong bits of the blowfish (an expensive delicacy in Japan).
Parts of the blowfish are so poisonous that they must be prepared by a chef with a special licence.

NOODLE NUTS FACT

The early inhabitants of Japan lived mainly on rice. Noodles were introduced from China in about AD 500.

07:45 Hari is chopping carrots into tiny pieces. So far he has cut up 2.75 kilos. How much more will he have to chop if he started with 5 kilos?

CHOP CHOP !

NOODLE NUTS FACT

Japan produces the sharpest kitchen knives in the world. They have a 45°-edge and are made from tungsten steel.

OUCH!

10:43 Hari starts to boil cabbage at 10.43 am. It takes 12 minutes to cook. At what time will the cabbage be ready?

When will the cabbage be done?

Just going in now...

NOODLE NUTS FACT

If a portion of noodles was laid out in a line it would be over 25 metres long. It is estimated that over 60 billion portions of instant noodles are eaten each year.

The money used in Japan is called yen. Prices of things are written like this: ¥100.

¥100

FIND THE CORRECT ANSWERS TO THE PROBLEMS AND CIRCLE THE LETTERS TO REVEAL:
WHAT HARI LIKES BEST WITH HIS NOODLES.

1:38

Use 3 litres of water for each ½ kilo of noodles.

Don't worry! I know how to cook noodles.

If the ratio is three litres of water to half a kilo of noodles, how much water should Ria use for 2 kilos of noodles?

NOODLE NUTS

PROBLEM SOLUTIONS

Ring the correct letters, then read the answer from the top.

12:10

The first customers are a group of 5 businessmen. They each order a bowl of plain noodles and...

We would all like pork with our noodles.

Ok, that's an extra 75 yen per person. The total for 5 bowls of noodles with pork is 1275 yen.

How much is a bowl of plain noodles?

¥152	T
10.55	O
EXACTLY ENOUGH	G
2.5 KILOGRAMS	S
MORE THAN ENOUGH	T
12 LITRES	C
¥237	T
10.57	R
¥2105	G
6 LITRES	E
¥180	O
1.75 KILOGRAMS	J
¥229	R
11.02	Q
¥2151	P
9 LITRES	Z
NOT ENOUGH	U
¥214	L
2.25 KILOGRAMS	S
¥2207	M
¥119	N

14:21

Our bill is 711 yen.

If they share the bill equally how much does each have to pay?

19:59

The last customer of the day...

Your bill comes to 2390 yen.

I have a 10% discount card.

That makes it...

How much does the customer have to pay after the discount?

When Noodle Nuts closes, Aiko and Hari make their way home. They take off their outdoor shoes and put on slippers. They settle down to watch TV and have their supper – 'Pot Noodles'! What else would noodle nuts have?

25

TARA'S T-SHIRT

Use ONE ml per square cm of stain
400ml

I've got half a bottle of stuff called Stain Blaster. How much do I need to put in the washer?

Oh! I'll have to work out the area of the stains.

That's not a problem, Nan.

This jam stain covers 2 squares completely and 4 half squares. So the jam stain is 4 squares on my T-shirt...

...and my T-shirt squares are each 3 cm by 3 cm.

How does that help?

It means that each T-shirt square is 9 cm^2...
... that makes the jam stain 36 cm^2.

So, if we add up all the stains, we'll know the total area in cm^2.

	number of T-shirt squares stain covers	number of cm^2 in T-shirt square	area of stain (cm^2)
jam	4	9	36
gum			
gravy			
ice cream			
chocolate			
custard			
TOTAL		—	

Read the instructions on the bottle of 'Stain Blaster'.

Can you complete Nan's list?

There was originally **400** ml in the bottle, but Nan only has **200** ml left.
If she uses one millilitre (ml) for every cm^2 of stain, will there be enough?

4 Romulus and Remus

Legend has it that Rome was founded by twins, Romulus and Remus in 753 BC.
Can you spot the identical twins in this line-up?

A   B   C   D   E   F   G   H

5 Super peach

Chuckius has thrown a rubbery old peach. The peach will continue to travel and bounce at 90° on hard surfaces until it hits someone or is caught. Can you trace the peach's path and see who gets it?

6 How many?

Lydia started the day with:
98 figs
35 melons
70 plums.

She had sold the lot by the end of the day. Each of Lydia's customers got the same quantity and the same selection of the three fruit. How many customers were there?

Solutions

This is where you can check your answers, or see how to solve a puzzle if you've got stuck. At the end of each we tell you which part of the Maths curriculum you're practising.

Alien Pal (pages 2 and 3)

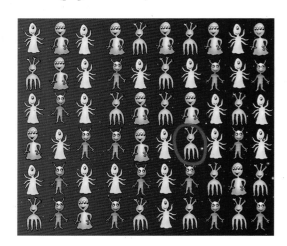

Fact 1: There are 14 green aliens with 3 eyes.
14 × 3 = 42

Fact 2: There are 12 blue aliens with 6 fingers each (72) and 14 pink aliens with 6 fingers each (84). So there are more pink fingers.

Fact 3: 20 yellow aliens each have 6 arms.
20 × 6 = 120

Fact 2 is false.

Roger has three eyes.

> Maths topic: Problem solving, number and calculations

Times for the Table... (pages 4 and 5)

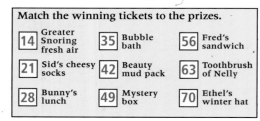

> Maths topic: Multiplying

Mobile Maths (pages 6 and 7)

A is talking to K
B is talking to P
C is talking to J
D is talking to N
E is talking to M
F is talking to R
G is talking to L
H is talking to T
I is talking to O
S is calling Q

> Maths topic: Solving problems

Pirate Positions (pages 8 and 9)

(1) Polly Parrot is A.
(2) Red Rob is C.
(3) The sherry is C.
(4) The treasure is buried under A (palm trees).
(5) The rubies are in chest A.
(6) The Black Dog is D.

> Maths topic: Problem solving, shape and space

Detective De Duction (pages 10 and 11)

1. Split the clock

10 + 11 + 12 + 1 + 2 + 3 = 39

4 + 5 + 6 + 7 + 8 + 9 = 39

2. Seven ones 11 + 11 + 11 + 1 = 34

3. Odd shadow The shadow of the walking stick is on the wrong side of the detective.

4. Camera shot C is the correct shot.

5. Footprint numbers (A) × 2   (B) + 1
(C) ÷ 2   (D) + 0.5

6. Fill in the blanks (E) 16   (F) 12   (G) 4
(H) 0.25   (I) 3.25   (J) 26

7. Picture shapes (1) D   (2) C   (3) F   (4) A

8. Missing jewel B (the square emerald).

9. Which key? H is the key to the padlock.

10. Name the set Not squares.

11. Squares within squares 10 squares.

> Maths topic: Problem solving, shape and space, number

Highway Robbery? (pages 12 and 13)

(A) Route 1 (100 km)
Swan Inn to Castle Town (26 km) to Ports Town (24 km) to Crossways (26 km) to Windy Hill (16 km) back to Swan Inn (8 km).

Route 2 (takes 11 hours at 10 km per hour: 110 km)
Swan Inn to Marsh Point (40 km) to Lighthouse Point (6 km) to Ports Town (14 km) to Castle Town (24 km) back to Swan Inn (26 km).

Route 3 (takes 12 hours at 10 km per hour: 120 km)

Swan Inn to Marsh Point (40 km) to Lighthouse Point (6 km) to Ports Town (14 km) to Castle Town (24 km) to Crossways (12 km) to Windy Hill (16 km) back to Swan Inn (8 km).

(B) Bad Bob never gets to rob the mail coach. None of the routes can go along the road between Castle Town and Marsh Point as the route would result in an odd number of kilometres travelled and all the routes have an even total.

> Maths topic: Measures, shape and space, calculations

Find the Percentages! (pages 14 and 15)

1. 4 out of the sample of 10 are wearing roller skates. 40% of 2000 is 800 contestants.

2. 1 out of 10 has spots. 10% of 2000 is 200.

3. 5 out of 10 are using pedals which is 50%.

> Maths topic: Fractions and percentages

What's the Distance? (pages 16 and 17)

(1) Cavitus of Eggium is the nearest.
Aquarium (Molia) is 30 milia passuum from Circadium, Odearium (Decayius) is 20 milia passuum, and Eggium (Cavitus) is 17 milia passuum.

(2) Odearium is nearest Tiptopium by road.
Aquarium is nearest to Ohmyium (to the right of Tiptopium). Eggium is below Ohmyium and above Hardium.

(3) Milestone
1. Tiptopium 2. Odearium 3. Ohmyium 4. Tiptopium
5. Hardium 6. Aquarium 7. Caromello 8. Hardium
9. Eggium. This spells out TOOTHACHE.

> Maths topic: Handling data, calculations, problem solving

Coordinates in the Castle (pages 18 and 19)

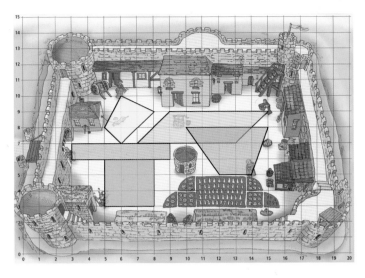

Martha the maiden walks an irregular quadrilateral.
John the jester walks a square.
Friar Doug walks a trapezium.
Graham the guard walks a rectangle.
Sarah the cook walks a parallelogram.
A rhombus is the shape which is not walked.

If Graham the guard pauses at (8, 7) he could meet Sarah the cook.

> Maths topic: Measures, shape and space

Gruesome Graphs (pages 20 and 21)

1. Lap 7.
2. 40 out of 50 gladiators.
3. Murder by stabbing.
4. Lottery prizes.

> Maths topic: Handling data

Add 'em Up! (pages 22 and 23)

Sum hoops
Three ways to score 18:
(A) 6 + 6 + 6   (B) 2 + 8 + 8   (C) 2 + 7 + 9

Three ways to score 20:
(A) 6 + 6 + 8   (B) 2 + 9 + 9   (C) 6 + 7 + 7

Sum buckets
Three ways to score 600:
(A) 200 + 200 + 125 + 75   (B) 300 + 150 + 75 + 75
(C) 200 + 150 + 125 + 125

Two ways to score 450:
(A) 125 + 125 + 125 + 75   (B) 150 + 150 + 75 + 75

Sum darts

Three ways to score 200:

(A) 100 + 40 + 40 + 20   (B) 50 + 50 + 50 + 50

(C) 100 + 50 + 40 + 10

Three ways to score 150:

(A) 50 + 50 + 40 + 10   (B) 100 + 20 + 20 + 10

(C) 50 + 40 + 40 + 20

> Maths topic: Calculations

Noodle Nuts (pages 24 and 25)

1. (04:30)   Not enough (U)
2. (07:45)   2.25 kg (S)
3. (10:43)   10.55 (O)
4. (11:38)   12 litres (C)
5. (12:10)   ¥180 (O)
6. (14:21)   ¥237 (T)
7. (19:59)   ¥2151 (P)

Correct answers spell out OCTOPUS (reading down).

> Maths topic: Solving problems

Tara's T-shirt (pages 26 and 27)

Jam	4	9	36
Gum	1	9	9
Gravy	2	9	18
Ice cream	5	9	45
Chocolate	3	9	27
Custard	6	9	54
Total	21		189

Tara's nan has enough 'Stain Blaster'; there will be 11 ml left in the bottle.

> Maths topic: Measures, shape and space

Are You Puzzled? (pages 28 and 29)

1. **Roman racers**

Domius won 16 races (half his age of 32).
Carvilos won 34 ((2 x 16) + 2).
Brutus won 68 (34 x 2).
Abutius won 73 (68 + 5) which is the most number of races.

2. **Find the pickpockets** and 5. **Super peach**

3. **How old?**

Ophelia is 6 years old. (Use trial and improvement to find the answer.)

4. **Romulus and Remus**
The twins are D and G.

6. **How many?**

There were 7 customers because 7 is the only factor of all the three amounts of fruit:
7 × 14 = 98 figs
7 × 5 = 35 melons
7 × 10 = 70 plums

> Maths topic: Solving problems

Published by Collins
An imprint of HarperCollins*Publishers*
77 – 85 Fulham Palace Road
Hammersmith
London
W6 8JB

Browse the complete Collins catalogue at www.collins.co.uk

© 2005 Juliet and Charles Snape

10 9 8 7 6 5 4 3 2 1

ISBN 0 00 721144 9

British Library Cataloguing in Publication Data
A Catalogue record for this publication is available from the British Library

Written by Juliet and Charles Snape
Consultant: Nigel Langdon MPhil, a maths consultant for the Royal Borough of Kingston upon Thames
Design, cover and illustrations by Juliet and Charles Snape
Printed and bound by Imago Thailand

Titles in this series:
Maths Explorer, Maths Mazes, Maths Mysteries, Maths Puzzles
To order any of these titles, please telephone **0870 787 1732** and quote code **256V**.